Rescued!

My adopted dog's
journal
of life and love with me.

This publication is part of a series of products and publications.
For more information, please visit:
https://lsgoulet.com
https://amazon.com/author/lsgoulet

This Journal
Belongs to:

YOUR STORY
Our Journey to You

How We Found You:

_____
_____
_____
_____

Your History As Told To Us:

_____
_____
_____
_____
_____
_____

What You Mean To Us:

_____
_____
_____
_____
_____

DATE:

Family Tree

The Greatest Gift is Family

A list of your humans

_____

_____

_____

_____

_____

Your animal siblings

_____

_____

_____

_____

_____

DATE:

YOUR FOREVER FAMILY

Love you for always...

MOMMY HUMAN

DADDY HUMAN

DOGGY

About You

Name:	
Birthdate:	
Adoption Date:	
Sex:	
Breed:	
Color:	
Weight:	
License #:	
Microchip #:	
Favorite places:	
Favorite toys:	
Dislikes:	

Health Information

Veterinarian's Name:	
Veterinarian's Address:	
Owner's Name:	
Owner's Address:	
Allergies:	
Medications:	
Other Health Issues:	
Feeding Notes:	

Your Favorite Exercises

Outdoor Exercise

Indoor Exercise

MEMORIES OF YOU

Your First Year With Us Photo Checklist

FIRST YEAR PHOTO CHECKLIST:

- [ ] Our first day with you
- [ ] Your first bath
- [ ] First family photo
- [ ] Your paws with our hands
- [ ] Doggy & Mommy
- [ ] Doggy's first vet visit
- [ ] Doggy's first grooming session
- [ ] Learning to play
- [ ] Doggy's first sit
- [ ] Doggy giving kisses
- [ ] Doggy with favorite toy

- [ ] doggy in dog park
- [ ] First treat
- [ ] Doggy's first walk
- [ ] Doggy & Daddy
- [ ] Doggy's first doggie daycare
- [ ] Doggy with friends
- [ ] Doggy s first trick
- [ ] Doggy sleeping
- [ ] Doggy's first birthday party
- [ ] Getting into mischief!
- [ ] Doggy's first car ride

OTHER PHOTO IDEAS:

- [ ]
- [ ]
- [ ]
- [ ]

- [ ]
- [ ]
- [ ]
- [ ]

Pictures to Remember You by

Pictures to Remember You by

Pictures to Remember You by

Pictures to Remember You by

Pictures to Remember You by

Pictures to Remember You by

Pictures to Remember You by

Pictures to Remember You by

You're our greatest gift...

Your first 12 months with us

MONTH 1

THOUGHTS

_____
_____
_____
_____
_____

MONTH 2

THOUGHTS

_____
_____
_____
_____
_____

MONTH 3

THOUGHTS

_____
_____
_____
_____
_____

MONTH 4

THOUGHTS

_____
_____
_____
_____
_____

MONTH 5

THOUGHTS

_____
_____
_____
_____
_____

DATE:
_____

_____

_____

_____

_____

_____

_____

_____

_____

_____

_____

_____

_____

_____

DATE:

You're our pride & joy...

Your first 12 months with us

MONTH 6	THOUGHTS
	_____
	_____
	_____

MONTH 7	THOUGHTS
	_____
	_____
	_____

MONTH 8	THOUGHTS
	_____
	_____
	_____

MONTH 9	THOUGHTS
	_____
	_____
	_____

MONTH 10	THOUGHTS
	_____
	_____
	_____

DATE:

DATE:

You're our everything...

Your first 12 months with us

MONTH 11

THOUGHTS

MONTH 12

THOUGHTS

Our Favorite Memories

DATE:

DATE:

Year By Year

Your First Year With Us

ALL ABOUT YOU

WEIGHT:

FAV FOOD:

FAV TREATS·

FAV ACTIVITY:

AND WHERE YOU CAME FROM

FAV TOY:

WHERE YOU WERE ADOPTED FROM:

_____

AGE:

NEGLECT/ABUSE HISTORY

HOW WE ENCOURAGED YOUR TRUST IN US

YOUR STRUGGLES AND ACCOMPLISHMENTS

Pictures to Remember You by

DATE:

Your Second Year With Us

ALL ABOUT YOU

WEIGHT:

FAV FOOD:

FAV TREATS:

FAV ACTIVITY:

FAV TOY:

HOW YOU HAVE GROWN

_____

AGE:

OUR GOALS FOR YOU

HOW YOU HAVE BLESSED OUR LIVES

YOUR STRUGGLES AND ACCOMPLISHMENTS

Pictures to Remember You by

DATE:

Your Third Year With Us

ALL ABOUT YOU

WEIGHT:

FAV FOOD:

FAV TREATS:

FAV ACTIVITY:

FAV TOY:

FAV TV SHOW

_____

AGE:

OUR GOALS FOR YOU

HOW YOU HAVE BLESSED OUR LIVES

YOUR STRUGGLES AND ACCOMPLISHMENTS

Pictures to Remember You by

DATE:
_____
_____
_____
_____
_____
_____
_____
_____
_____
_____
_____
_____
_____
_____
_____

Your Fourth Year With Us

ALL ABOUT YOU

WEIGHT:

FAV FOOD:

FAV TREATS:

FAV ACTIVITY:

FAV TOY:

FAV PLACE TO TAKE A NAP:

_____

AGE:

OUR GOALS FOR YOU

HOW YOU HAVE BLESSED OUR LIVES

YOUR STRUGGLES AND ACCOMPLISHMENTS

love
IS
forever

DATE:

Your Fifth Year With Us

ALL ABOUT YOU

WEIGHT:

FAV FOOD:

FAV TREATS:

FAV ACTIVITY:

FAV TOY:

HOW YOU SHOW LOVE:

_____

AGE:

OUR GOALS FOR YOU

HOW YOU HAVE BLESSED OUR LIVES

YOUR STRUGGLES AND ACCOMPLISHMENTS

DATE:

Your Sixth Year With Us

ALL ABOUT YOU

WEIGHT:

FAV FOOD:

FAV TREATS·

FAV ACTIVITY:

FAV TOY:

HOW YOU SHOW FEAR:

_____

AGE:

OUR GOALS FOR YOU

HOW YOU HAVE BLESSED OUR LIVES

YOUR STRUGGLES AND ACCOMPLISHMENTS

love
IS
forever

DATE:

Your Seventh Year With Us

ALL ABOUT YOU

WEIGHT:

FAV FOOD:

FAV TREATS:

FAV ACTIVITY:

FAV TOY:

REACTION TO LOUD NOISES:

_____

AGE:

OUR GOALS FOR YOU

HOW YOU HAVE BLESSED OUR LIVES

YOUR STRUGGLES AND ACCOMPLISHMENTS

love
IS
forever

DATE:

Your Eighth Year With Us

ALL ABOUT YOU

WEIGHT:

FAV FOOD:

FAV TREATS·

FAV ACTIVITY:

FAV TOY:

FAV THING TO DO:

_____

AGE:

OUR GOALS FOR YOU

HOW YOU HAVE BLESSED OUR LIVES

YOUR STRUGGLES AND ACCOMPLISHMENTS

love
is
forever

DATE:

Your Ninth Year With Us

ALL ABOUT YOU

WEIGHT:

FAV FOOD:

FAV TREATS:

FAV ACTIVITY:

FAV TOY:

ACTIVITY LEVEL:

_____

AGE:

OUR GOALS FOR YOU

HOW YOU HAVE BLESSED OUR LIVES

YOUR STRUGGLES AND ACCOMPLISHMENTS

love
IS
forever

DATE:

Your Tenth Year With Us

ALL ABOUT YOU

WEIGHT: FAV TOY:

FAV FOOD: FAV PEOPLE FOOD:

FAV TREATS·   _____

FAV ACTIVITY: AGE:

OUR GOALS FOR YOU

HOW YOU HAVE BLESSED OUR LIVES

YOUR STRUGGLES AND ACCOMPLISHMENTS

love
IS
forever

DATE:

Your Eleventh Year With Us

ALL ABOUT YOU

WEIGHT:

FAV FOOD:

FAV TREATS:

FAV ACTIVITY:

FAV TOY:

FAV OUT OF THE WAY SPOT

_____

AGE:

OUR GOALS FOR YOU

HOW YOU HAVE BLESSED OUR LIVES

YOUR STRUGGLES AND ACCOMPLISHMENTS

love
IS
forever

DATE:

Your Twelfth Year With Us

ALL ABOUT YOU

WEIGHT:

FAV FOOD:

FAV TREATS:

FAV ACTIVITY:

FAV TOY:

FAV PLACE TO SLEEP

_____

AGE:

OUR GOALS FOR YOU

HOW YOU HAVE BLESSED OUR LIVES

YOUR STRUGGLES AND ACCOMPLISHMENTS

love
IS
forever

DATE:

Immunization Records

Date	Name of Immunization	Date of Next Immunization	Notes:

Immunization Records

Date	Name of Immunization	Date of Next Immunization	Notes:

Immunization Records

Date	Name of Immunization	Date of Next Immunization	Notes:

Immunization Records

Date	Name of Immunization	Date of Next Immunization	Notes:

Immunization Records

Date	Name of Immunization	Date of Next Immunization	Notes:

Immunization Records

Date	Name of Immunization	Date of Next Immunization	Notes:

Veterinarian Visits

Date	Reason for Visit	Health Concerns:	Notes:

Veterinarian Visits

Date	Reason for Visit	Health Concerns:	Notes:

Veterinarian Visits

Date	Reason for Visit	Health Concerns:	Notes:

Veterinarian Visits

Date	Reason for Visit	Health Concerns:	Notes:

Veterinarian Visits

Date	Reason for Visit	Health Concerns:	Notes:

Veterinarian Visits

Date	Reason for Visit	Health Concerns:	Notes:

Your leaving came much too soon. We will keep you buried in our hearts forever. I hope this last home for you was a refuge of love, peace, and contentment. We'll meet you on the other side of the Rainbow Bridge when our time comes.

Our last day together and how you left us

_____

_____

_____

_____

_____

_____

_____

_____

_____

The things we'll remember most about you.

OUR LAST PICTURE OF YOU

DATE:

DATE:

DATE:

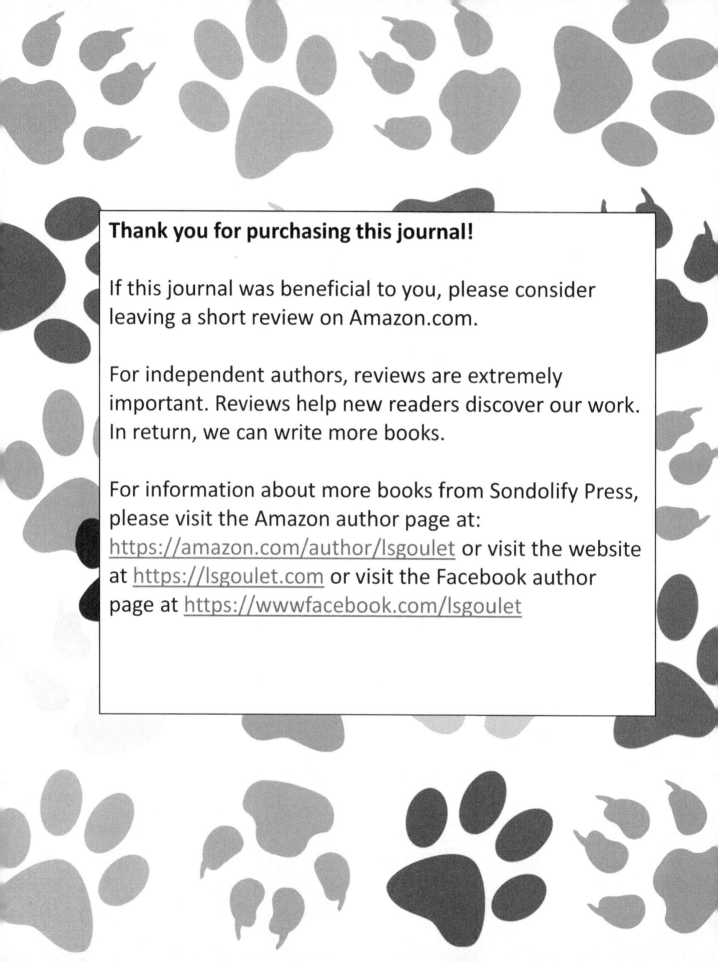

Thank you for purchasing this journal!

If this journal was beneficial to you, please consider leaving a short review on Amazon.com.

For independent authors, reviews are extremely important. Reviews help new readers discover our work. In return, we can write more books.

For information about more books from Sondolify Press, please visit the Amazon author page at: https://amazon.com/author/lsgoulet or visit the website at https://lsgoulet.com or visit the Facebook author page at https://wwwfacebook.com/lsgoulet

Made in the USA
Middletown, DE
07 January 2020